A little bug is in a jug.
Look! It jumps on a
rug.

1

Bean pulls the rug ...
tug ... tug ... tug.
The little bug lands in
the mug.

Kevin sees the little bug swimming in the yellow mug.

He puts the bug back
on the rug.
He has a drink from
the mug.

A big green bug is on the rug.
It's going to eat the little bug.

Bean pulls the rug ...
tug ... tug ... tug.
The big green bug
lands in the jug.

The big green bug is
in the jug.
The little bug is on the
rug.

Oh no! It jumps in the cup.

Oh no! Kevin drinks it up.